THE UNOFFICIAL

BRIDGERTON
COLOURING BOOK

ILLUSTRATED BY
WESLEY JONES

WHITE LION
PUBLISHING

Brimming with creative inspiration, how-to projects, and useful information to enrich your everyday life, Quarto Knows is a favorite destination for those pursuing their interests and passions. Visit our site and dig deeper with our books into your area of interest: Quarto Creates, Quarto Cooks, Quarto Homes, Quarto Lives, Quarto Drives, Quarto Explores, Quarto Gifts, or Quarto Kids.

First published in the US in 2021 by becker&mayer! books
This UK edition first published in 2021 by White Lion Publishing,
an imprint of The Quarto Group
The Old Brewery
6 Blundell Street
London N7 9BH
www.QuartoKnows.com

A catalogue record for this book is available from the British Library.

10 9 8 7 6 5 4 3 2 1

ISBN: 978-0-7112-6991-0

Illustration by Wesley Jones

Printed, manufactured, and assembled in Guangdong, China, 07/21

#347794